Spooky Stories

This book of spooky stories belongs to

Spooky Stories

Written by
Caroline Repchuk, Claire Keene,
Geoff Cowan, Kat Wootton and Candy Wallace

Illustrated by
Diana Catchpole, Robin Edmonds,
Chris Forsey and Claire Mumford

This is a Parragon Book
This edition published in 2003

Parragon,
Queen Street House,
4 Queen Street,
Bath BA1 1HE

Produced by
The Templar Company plc.

Designed by
Caroline Reeves

Printed and bound in China
ISBN 1-40542-034-0

Contents

Hoots'n'Owls

Freaky Friends

Smoky Smells Success

A Night in the Haunted House

Shadow's Lucky Charm

Spooky Spells

Stand and Deliver

The Mummy's Curse

Peg's Pepper

Hoots 'n' Owls

"OWWW!" A horrible howl rang out through the darkness. Beneath the moon, Hairy the Horrible Hound sat staring at his paws. After a minute the ghostly dog raised his head and howled again.

Hairy had been howling away all evening. He wanted someone to talk to, someone to play with. But because he was a ghost hound no one would come near, let alone throw him a stick to chase. So he lay with his head on his shadowy paws and howled even more loudly.

The moon shone between the clouds and lit up the ruined manor house on top of the hill. The people who once lived there had fled years ago. Now it was just the haunt of three old ghosts....

Shiver, a nervous spook, was resting upstairs on a broken four-poster bed. At the first sound of Hairy's howls, he slid under the tattered sheets and pulled them tightly over his head.

Downstairs, another ghost named Grumblegroan woke with a start. As usual, he had been dozing on a crumpled old sofa.

"What the...? Doesn't Hairy the Horrible Hound ever stop howling?!" muttered Grumblegroan, miserably.

Meanwhile, Bone Idle, a skeleton, came clattering out of his favourite hiding place, a secret chamber behind the bookcase in the library.

"Pah!" he cried. "That dreadful noise goes right through my skull!"

When the howling finally stopped, all three spooks met in the hall.

"It's too much for a soul to bear!"
hissed Shiver.

"How can a ghost rest in peace around
here?!" yawned Grumblegroan.

"Something must be done about Hairy!"
wailed Bone Idle.

But what? After all, Hairy certainly sounded
like a very fierce phantom. And the three
ghosts were a lazy lot. They weren't very good
at doing anything — especially as there was
never anything to do! So, with much
muttering, sighing and moaning, the spooks
sulkily decided to do nothing at all. They
certainly weren't about to move house!
After all, Hairy's howls were the only thing
that ever disturbed them. Apart from that the
house was as silent as a grave. But suddenly,
on the landing, Shiver heard another call.

"HOO-HOOOOOOO!"

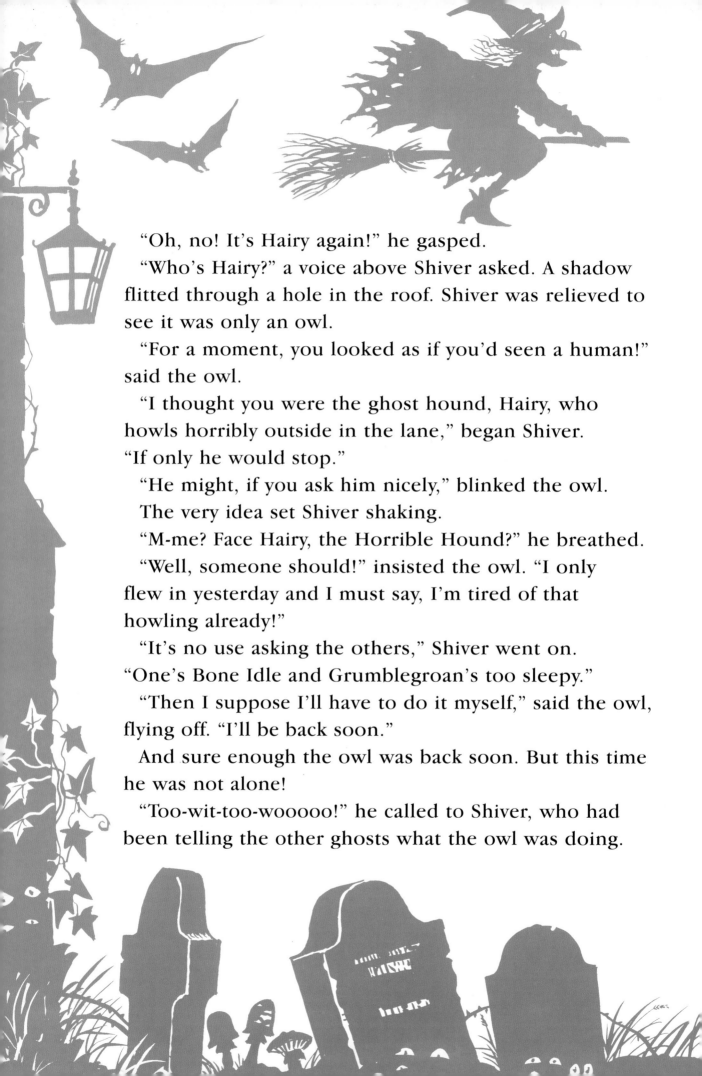

"Oh, no! It's Hairy again!" he gasped.

"Who's Hairy?" a voice above Shiver asked. A shadow flitted through a hole in the roof. Shiver was relieved to see it was only an owl.

"For a moment, you looked as if you'd seen a human!" said the owl.

"I thought you were the ghost hound, Hairy, who howls horribly outside in the lane," began Shiver. "If only he would stop."

"He might, if you ask him nicely," blinked the owl.

The very idea set Shiver shaking.

"M-me? Face Hairy, the Horrible Hound?" he breathed.

"Well, someone should!" insisted the owl. "I only flew in yesterday and I must say, I'm tired of that howling already!"

"It's no use asking the others," Shiver went on. "One's Bone Idle and Grumblegroan's too sleepy."

"Then I suppose I'll have to do it myself," said the owl, flying off. "I'll be back soon."

And sure enough the owl was back soon. But this time he was not alone!

"Too-wit-too-wooooo!" he called to Shiver, who had been telling the other ghosts what the owl was doing.

All three heard the bird hoot. Then came
Hairy's dreaded howl. It was louder and
closer than ever before! There was a padding
of paws on the front door before it swung
open on its creaky hinges.

"Yikes! Time I disappeared!" trembled
Shiver. But it was too late! In swept the owl,
followed by the huge, ghostly hound.
Shiver clung so tightly to Bone Idle that the
skeleton rattled from top to toe. For once,
Grumblegroan's eyes were open wide.

"Ready for a hair-raising encounter?"
joked the owl, pointing with a wing-tip to
the large, ambling dog. To the three spooks'
amazement, the ghost hound looked as
harmless as an overgrown pup.

"Hairy told me that he only howls
because he's lonely," said the owl.
"He chases anything that moves, too,

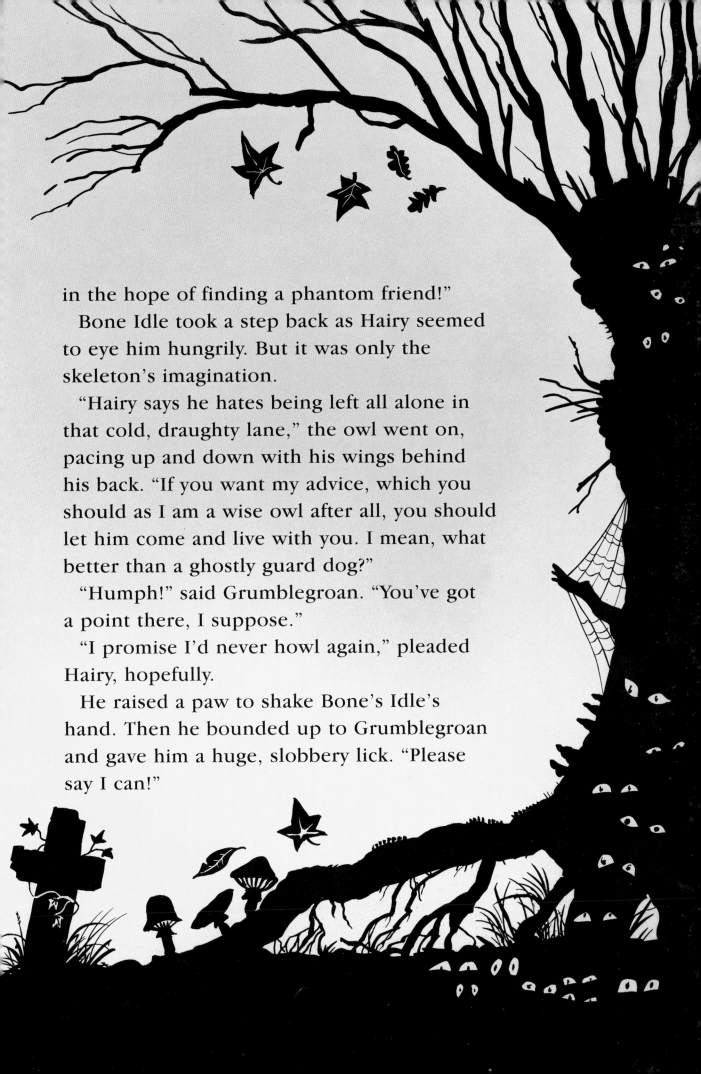

in the hope of finding a phantom friend!"

Bone Idle took a step back as Hairy seemed to eye him hungrily. But it was only the skeleton's imagination.

"Hairy says he hates being left all alone in that cold, draughty lane," the owl went on, pacing up and down with his wings behind his back. "If you want my advice, which you should as I am a wise owl after all, you should let him come and live with you. I mean, what better than a ghostly guard dog?"

"Humph!" said Grumblegroan. "You've got a point there, I suppose."

"I promise I'd never howl again," pleaded Hairy, hopefully.

He raised a paw to shake Bone's Idle's hand. Then he bounded up to Grumblegroan and gave him a huge, slobbery lick. "Please say I can!"

"Oh, very well. Anything! Just...uhh!...stop making that horrid noise!" moaned Grumblegroan.

"You can lie beside my old bed, Hairy," smiled Shiver, who wasn't the least bit nervous now.

"Great!" barked the ghost hound. "I'm so happy I could howww...."

"No, please don't!" begged Bone Idle. "You did promise. Remember?"

And so Hairy, the Horrible Hound, had found a home at last. As for the owl, he soon took flight again. But if the three ghosts had hoped for some peace and quiet, they were to be sadly disappointed. For Hairy never left them alone. If he wasn't playfully pulling the sheets off Shiver, he would leap on to Grumblegroan's lap for company.

And whenever Bone Idle tried to
tiptoe away to his hidden chamber,
the ghost hound thought the skeleton
wanted him to play haunt and seek!

Slowly, though, the lazy spooks grew
to like things being more lively. Which was
just as well, or Hairy may have had to start
howling again!

Freaky Friends

Having an old witch as her next-door-neighbour was the last thing that Victoria Vampire wanted. No sooner had Winnie moved in, complete with her broomstick, cauldron, pointed hat and all manner of pots and potions, than weird things began to happen.

Whenever Winnie stirred up a magical brew indoors, a mass of stars and sparks would fly out of the chimney of her tumbledown old cottage like a fantastic firework show.

They whizzed safely beyond her own little cottage garden — and landed in the grounds of Victoria's dark and spooky house instead! Victoria's clean washing was soon spotted with sooty marks and two big holes were burned in her best black cloak.

Then there was the smell, or more precisely, the stinky pong! Whatever was bubbling away in Winnie's cauldron, it was definitely *not* leek and potato soup. The awful aroma wafted across into the dark turrets of Victoria's home. In no time it had disturbed Victoria's precious colony of bats that lived in the attic. They poured like black treacle out of a small skylight and fluttered away to hide in a dark, distant cave. And as if losing her pets wasn't bad enough, Victoria had to keep every door and window tightly closed against the stink. It was enough to make her flash her fangs in anger!

But there was worse to come. Winnie's two cats, Scratch and Sniff, were mouse-mad, they chased them non-stop. So one day, when they spotted some by Victoria's woodshed, the mean-eyed cats set off in hot pursuit. The trouble was that Victoria had just entered the shed to fetch some logs for her fire. Now, being a vampire, she didn't like going out in daylight and, as usual, was wearing her dark sunglasses. So she didn't see Scratch and Sniff slink into the shed — she just felt the sting of their claws as she tripped over them and they lashed out at her legs. Victoria let out a blood-curdling scream, the startled cats screeched 'YEOWWL!', wood went flying and so did Victoria! She crashed into the door, bumping her head and breaking an arm off her precious sunglasses.

Meanwhile, the cats sulkily slipped away, having lost the mice who had taken advantage of all the commotion and disappeared.

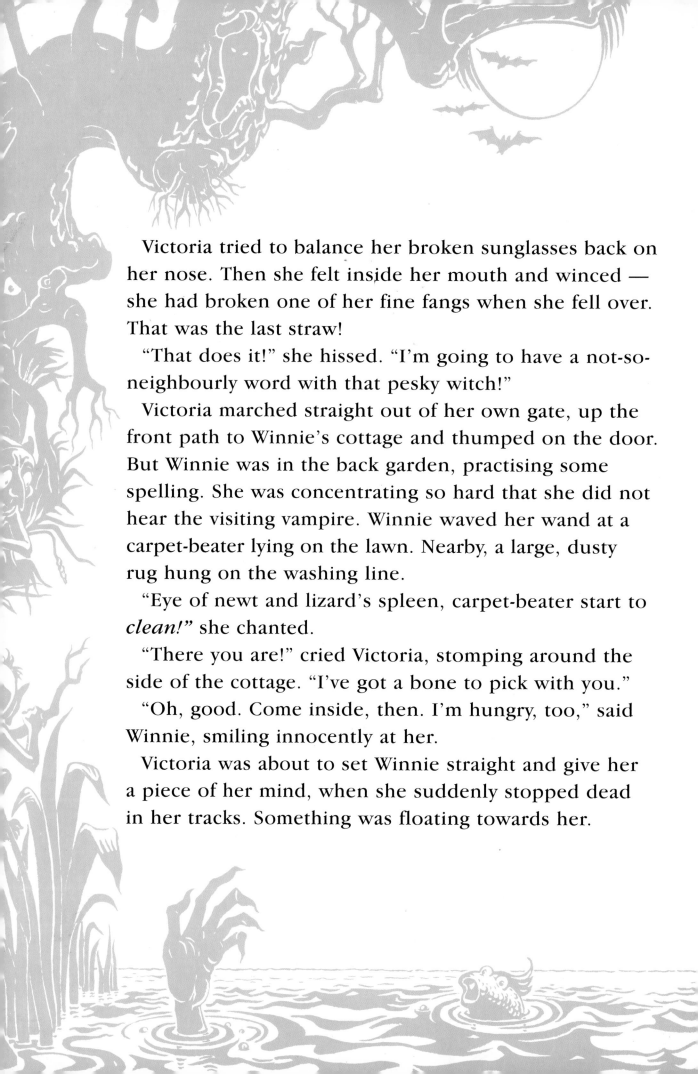

Victoria tried to balance her broken sunglasses back on her nose. Then she felt inside her mouth and winced — she had broken one of her fine fangs when she fell over. That was the last straw!

"That does it!" she hissed. "I'm going to have a not-so-neighbourly word with that pesky witch!"

Victoria marched straight out of her own gate, up the front path to Winnie's cottage and thumped on the door. But Winnie was in the back garden, practising some spelling. She was concentrating so hard that she did not hear the visiting vampire. Winnie waved her wand at a carpet-beater lying on the lawn. Nearby, a large, dusty rug hung on the washing line.

"Eye of newt and lizard's spleen, carpet-beater start to *clean!*" she chanted.

"There you are!" cried Victoria, stomping around the side of the cottage. "I've got a bone to pick with you."

"Oh, good. Come inside, then. I'm hungry, too," said Winnie, smiling innocently at her.

Victoria was about to set Winnie straight and give her a piece of her mind, when she suddenly stopped dead in her tracks. Something was floating towards her.

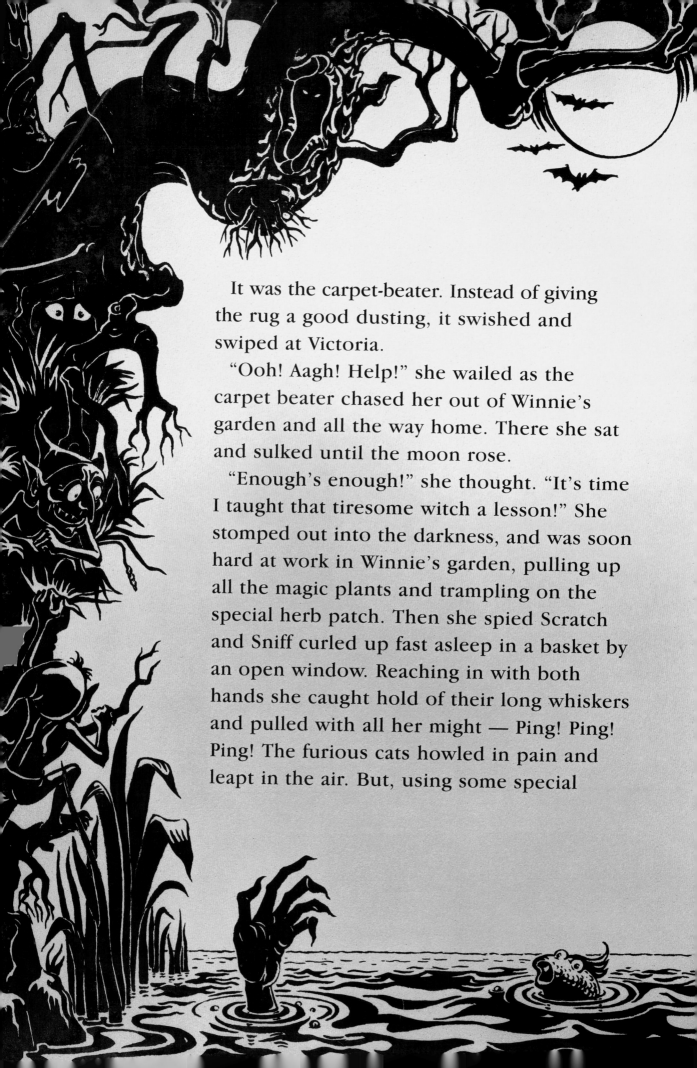

It was the carpet-beater. Instead of giving the rug a good dusting, it swished and swiped at Victoria.

"Ooh! Aagh! Help!" she wailed as the carpet beater chased her out of Winnie's garden and all the way home. There she sat and sulked until the moon rose.

"Enough's enough!" she thought. "It's time I taught that tiresome witch a lesson!" She stomped out into the darkness, and was soon hard at work in Winnie's garden, pulling up all the magic plants and trampling on the special herb patch. Then she spied Scratch and Sniff curled up fast asleep in a basket by an open window. Reaching in with both hands she caught hold of their long whiskers and pulled with all her might — Ping! Ping! Ping! The furious cats howled in pain and leapt in the air. But, using some special

vampire magic of her own, Victoria turned
herself into a bat and took off into the night.
But she hadn't flown far when, suddenly,
something whizzed past her like a rocket.
It was Winnie on her broomstick.

Caught in its slipstream, Victoria was tossed
about like a leaf in a storm. She had just made
a bumpy landing on Winnie's lawn when the
witch swooped down and landed right on
top of her! As Scratch prepared to pounce,
thinking bat might make a tasty alternative to
mouse, Victoria changed back with a flash.
But she was bruised and breathless.

"Ohh! My back!" Victoria groaned.

"Deary me!" wailed the witch. "It's all my
fault! I had no idea it was you! Here, please
let me help!"

Victoria was too weary to argue. And help
Winnie certainly did.

Over the next few days, nothing was too
much trouble for her. She insisted that
Victoria rest at home in bed while she
cooked a surprisingly tasty beetroot soup.
It was such a deliciously deep red colour
that Victoria had to have some.

"It would have been better if those pesky
cats hadn't dug up my herbs, mind you," said
Winnie. While Victoria guiltily enjoyed another
bowlful, Winnie searched her spell book

"Aha! I knew it was here somewhere!" she
said. Winnie waved her wand and chanted
something about taking care of canines.
Then, in a flash, Victoria's two beautiful,
long sharp teeth were perfect again.

"*Fangs* very much," she joked.

Further spells repaired the holes in
Victoria's cloak, cleaned up her washing,
and brought her bats back to the loft.
Another spell made Winnie's broom sweep up
the wood-shed. Scratch and Sniff eagerly
caught every mouse in Victoria's house (which
made up a bit for losing their whiskers!).
Victoria felt ashamed for trying to teach the
kind witch a lesson.

"I feel so much better," smiled Victoria,
getting up at last. "You're a wonder, Winnie!"

"Nonsense! Nothing like a *spell* in bed,"
the witch replied, modestly, as she gave her
new-found friend a hug.

Smoky Smells Success

Smoky was a spook, and a very happy
spook at that! He haunted an ancient
castle, surrounded by a wide moat.
From deep in its darkest dungeons to
high on the heights of its battlements,
Smoky would appear, mischievously and
mysteriously, whenever he wanted.
Sometimes, he appeared just as himself —
a swirling puff of supernatural smoke.
However, being a ghost, Smoky could
change shape at will.

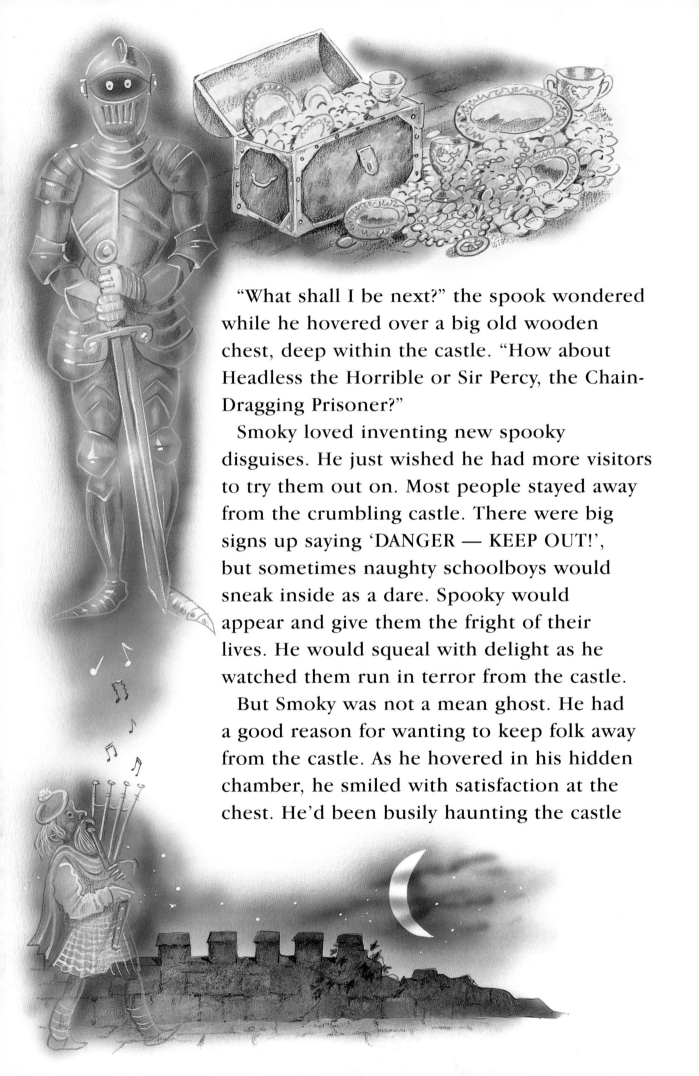

"What shall I be next?" the spook wondered while he hovered over a big old wooden chest, deep within the castle. "How about Headless the Horrible or Sir Percy, the Chain-Dragging Prisoner?"

Smoky loved inventing new spooky disguises. He just wished he had more visitors to try them out on. Most people stayed away from the crumbling castle. There were big signs up saying 'DANGER — KEEP OUT!', but sometimes naughty schoolboys would sneak inside as a dare. Spooky would appear and give them the fright of their lives. He would squeal with delight as he watched them run in terror from the castle.

But Smoky was not a mean ghost. He had a good reason for wanting to keep folk away from the castle. As he hovered in his hidden chamber, he smiled with satisfaction at the chest. He'd been busily haunting the castle

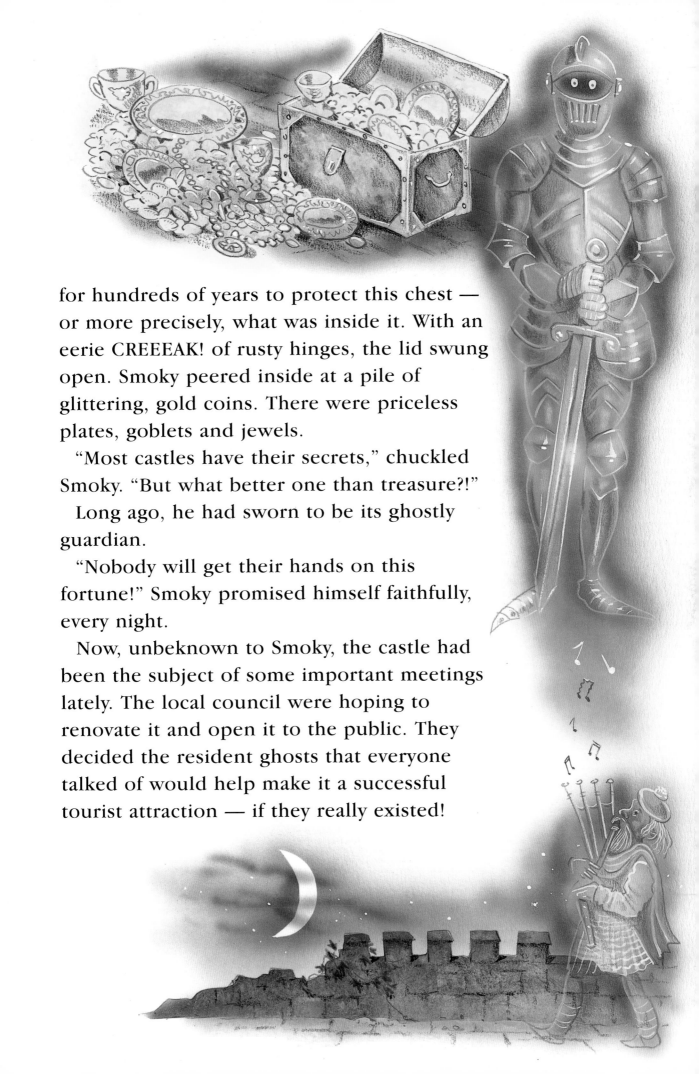

for hundreds of years to protect this chest —
or more precisely, what was inside it. With an
eerie CREEEAK! of rusty hinges, the lid swung
open. Smoky peered inside at a pile of
glittering, gold coins. There were priceless
plates, goblets and jewels.

"Most castles have their secrets," chuckled
Smoky. "But what better one than treasure?!"

Long ago, he had sworn to be its ghostly
guardian.

"Nobody will get their hands on this
fortune!" Smoky promised himself faithfully,
every night.

Now, unbeknown to Smoky, the castle had
been the subject of some important meetings
lately. The local council were hoping to
renovate it and open it to the public. They
decided the resident ghosts that everyone
talked of would help make it a successful
tourist attraction — if they really existed!

So it was that one morning, Smoky heard a car pull up. A man and woman climbed out. They walked slowly around the castle walls, making notes, and looking very serious indeed.

"It's no use," said the man. "This castle's crumbling. If we don't pull it down, it will fall all on its own. We're going to have to forget about opening it to the public."

"Pity," replied the woman. "It's such a grand, historical building. If only we could raise enough money to have it repaired. But that would cost a fortune!"

Smoky froze. For the first time, he understood what it was like to be scared! If his precious castle was pulled down, what would happen to him? He wouldn't want to haunt anywhere else. Something had to be done — and fast!

As the visitors were returning to their car, they suddenly stopped and sniffed the air. There was a wonderful smell coming from the castle. The man pointed to what looked like a thin trail of steam floating by the entrance. It was Smoky, who had conjured up a delicious smell to tempt the visitors in.

"Let's take a look inside," said the man.

"But it's dangerous — and apparently haunted!" said the woman, nervously.

"We'll be careful," said the man. "I have to find out where that incredible smell is coming from."

They followed the lovely smell into the castle. Smoky led the way, disguised as a thin trail of smoke. For once, he didn't want to frighten his visitors away! They crept quietly along the corridors, glancing nervously over their shoulders, but there were no spooks to be seen. Smoky made a secret door in one of the walls swing wide open. A narrow, cobweb-filled passage led the visitors to his hidden chamber and...the treasure chest!

When the officials saw its glittering, golden contents, they shrieked so loudly it made Smoky jump.

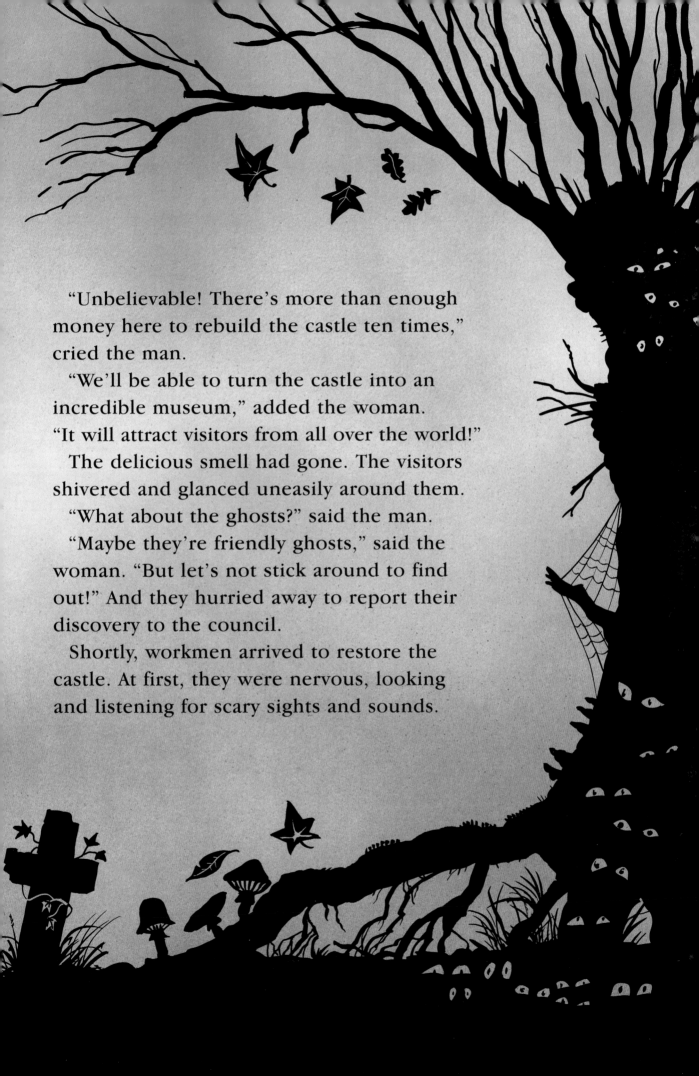

"Unbelievable! There's more than enough money here to rebuild the castle ten times," cried the man.

"We'll be able to turn the castle into an incredible museum," added the woman. "It will attract visitors from all over the world!"

The delicious smell had gone. The visitors shivered and glanced uneasily around them.

"What about the ghosts?" said the man.

"Maybe they're friendly ghosts," said the woman. "But let's not stick around to find out!" And they hurried away to report their discovery to the council.

Shortly, workmen arrived to restore the castle. At first, they were nervous, looking and listening for scary sights and sounds.

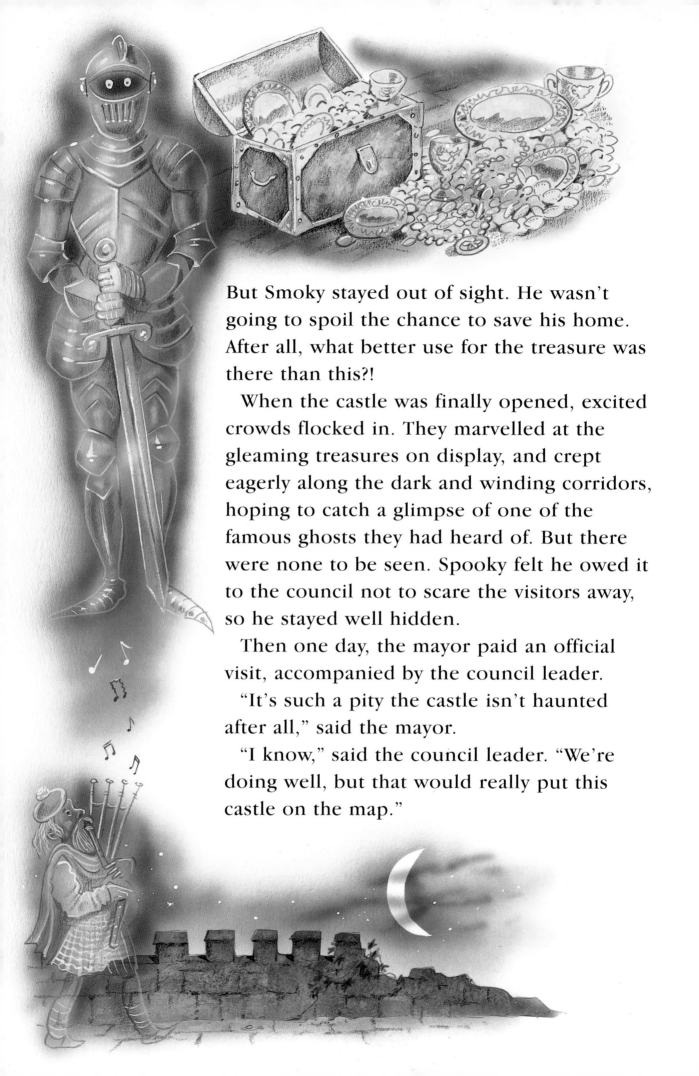

But Smoky stayed out of sight. He wasn't going to spoil the chance to save his home. After all, what better use for the treasure was there than this?!

When the castle was finally opened, excited crowds flocked in. They marvelled at the gleaming treasures on display, and crept eagerly along the dark and winding corridors, hoping to catch a glimpse of one of the famous ghosts they had heard of. But there were none to be seen. Spooky felt he owed it to the council not to scare the visitors away, so he stayed well hidden.

Then one day, the mayor paid an official visit, accompanied by the council leader.

"It's such a pity the castle isn't haunted after all," said the mayor.

"I know," said the council leader. "We're doing well, but that would really put this castle on the map."

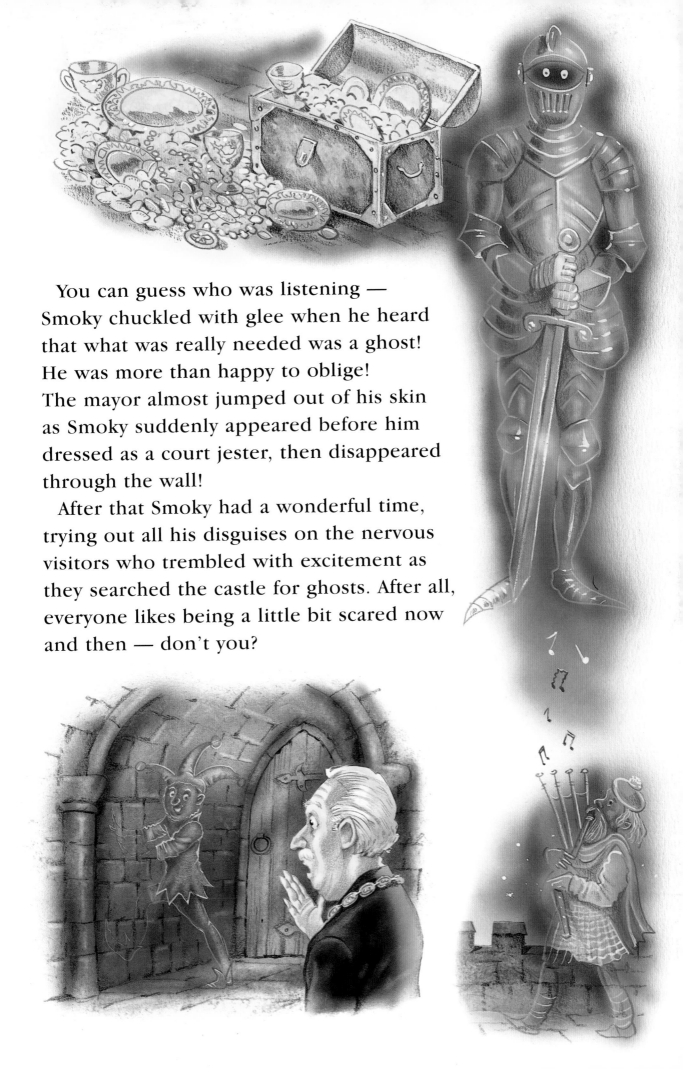

You can guess who was listening —
Smoky chuckled with glee when he heard
that what was really needed was a ghost!
He was more than happy to oblige!
The mayor almost jumped out of his skin
as Smoky suddenly appeared before him
dressed as a court jester, then disappeared
through the wall!

After that Smoky had a wonderful time,
trying out all his disguises on the nervous
visitors who trembled with excitement as
they searched the castle for ghosts. After all,
everyone likes being a little bit scared now
and then — don't you?

A Night in the Haunted House

High up on a lonely hill, surrounded by a great dark forest, stood an ancient, crumbling manor, known as the *Haunted House*. It belonged to a greedy old man, who everyone said was a wizard. He lived in a little cottage in the grounds of the manor, with just his black cat for company. He had no friends to speak of, but he was very happy, because he had a true love. Now, his true love was gold, and he had plenty of it, for he had found a way to make the *Haunted House* serve him well, even though he dare not set one foot inside it himself.

He had pinned a notice to the tall rusting gates of the manor, promising a reward of five hundred gold coins to anyone who could spend a whole night inside it, and charging them five gold coins for the privilege of trying.

Desperate men and brave adventurers came from far and wide, each certain they could withstand the horrors of the *Haunted House*. Some did well, and lasted many hours before fleeing in terror. Back in the safety of the local village inn, they would mutter and gibber and stutter out tales of ghosts so ghoulish, and monsters so terrifying, that their wide-eyed listeners would gasp with horror and congratulate them for staying in the house so long. Others lasted mere minutes before fleeing into the night in shame.

Now one day, there came a man called Titan, whose bravery was legendary. He was known far and wide as the most fearless adventurer, with towering strength and nerves of steel. He paid his five gold coins to the wizard, who rather reluctantly gave him the key to the house. This fellow looked a bit too fearless for the wizard's liking.

That night, Titan stepped through the rusty gates, and strode towards the *Haunted House*. Without hesitating, he unlocked the door and went in. A butler appeared from nowhere, carrying his head under his arm. "Jeeves at your service, sir," he said, creepily. "Follow me."

"Thank you, my good man," said Titan, handing him his coat and following him up the creaking staircase without blinking an eye.

Ancient portraits followed him with their eyes. Titan winked at them as he passed. An empty suit of armour waved. Titan waved back. "Good evening," he said.

Jeeves led him on down a murky passage. A heavy door creaked open and they entered a dark bedroom, with a tattered four-poster bed. Cobwebs hung from the ceiling, and a thick layer of dust covered the furniture. Titan opened the wardrobe and a skeleton came leering out. "Oops, sorry to disturb you," Titan said, brushing the cobwebs from a chair.

The startled butler looked at Titan in amazement. Was this man scared of anything?. "Tea, sir?" Jeeves asked. "Herman will bring it up right away."

Moments later Herman, a dribbling two-headed ogre, appeared with Titan's tea. "Thank you," said Titan, pouring the tea without flinching. "That will be all."

And so it went on through the night. The inhabitants of the *Haunted House* did their worst. Ghouls wailed and werewolves howled. Mummies rose up from their tombs and staggered through the room. A ghostly prisoner appeared dragging clanking chains and vanished through the wall. Vampires leered and phantoms jeered.

"This is quite a show!" said Titan, settling back on his pillows, and watching the ghostly goings-on with a cheerful grin.

Meanwhile, down in the little cottage, the wizard kept glancing nervously at the clock, as he shone and polished his precious gold. Slowly the hours passed, and still there was no sign of Titan. Could this be the man who would finally claim the reward?

Back at the house, a fluffy white ghost was hovering over Titan's head, shouting "Boo!" and trying to sound frightening. It was his first night on the job. The startled spooks had had to call out all reserves — how were they going to frighten this man of steel?

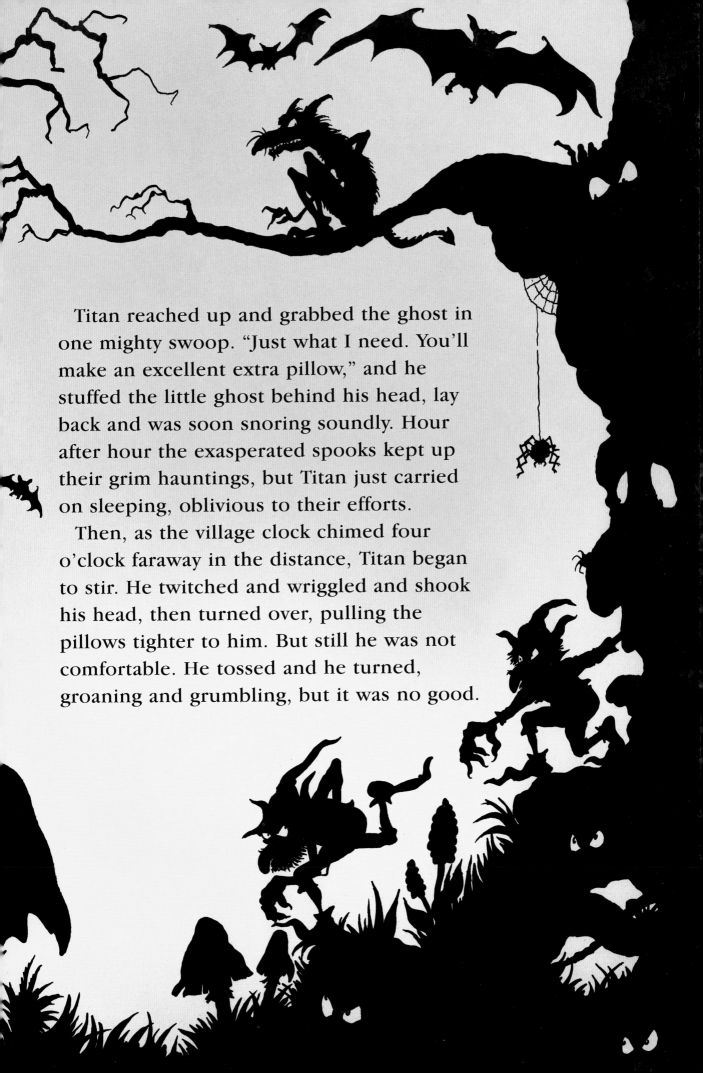

Titan reached up and grabbed the ghost in one mighty swoop. "Just what I need. You'll make an excellent extra pillow," and he stuffed the little ghost behind his head, lay back and was soon snoring soundly. Hour after hour the exasperated spooks kept up their grim hauntings, but Titan just carried on sleeping, oblivious to their efforts.

Then, as the village clock chimed four o'clock faraway in the distance, Titan began to stir. He twitched and wriggled and shook his head, then turned over, pulling the pillows tighter to him. But still he was not comfortable. He tossed and he turned, groaning and grumbling, but it was no good.

There was something lumpy underneath his pillow that was keeping him from settling back to sleep. He opened his eyes. The exhausted ghouls surged forward, renewing their efforts to terrify him.

"Oh, are you chaps still up?!" said Titan, surprised. "Don't you have beds to go to?" The weary ghosts shook their heads in exasperation. Titan felt about under his pillow. What was it that was lodged under there, keeping him awake? Just then, his hand wrapped around something small and soft and furry. He felt a shiver run down his spine. Slowly he pulled out his hand from under the pillow and there, trembling in fright was a tiny little white mouse. Titan let out an almighty scream! He leapt from the bed and raced for the door.

Down he fled through dusty passages and darkened stairways, then disappeared, still screaming and hollering, into the night.

Through his window, the wizard cackled in delight as he watched him fleeing. He hugged his bag of gold to him, and rubbed his hands together with glee.

"I knew he'd crack," he chuckled. "Something gets to all of them in the end!"

Shadow's 'Lucky' Charm

Dark shadows of evening hung over the television studios. A chill wind groaned about the buildings. Bustling by day, with actors and cameramen, make-up experts and programme producers, now everyone had gone home and the place stood empty. Only Sam, the security officer, remained. His torch shone upon doors and windows as he made his rounds, checking everything was shut down safely till morning.

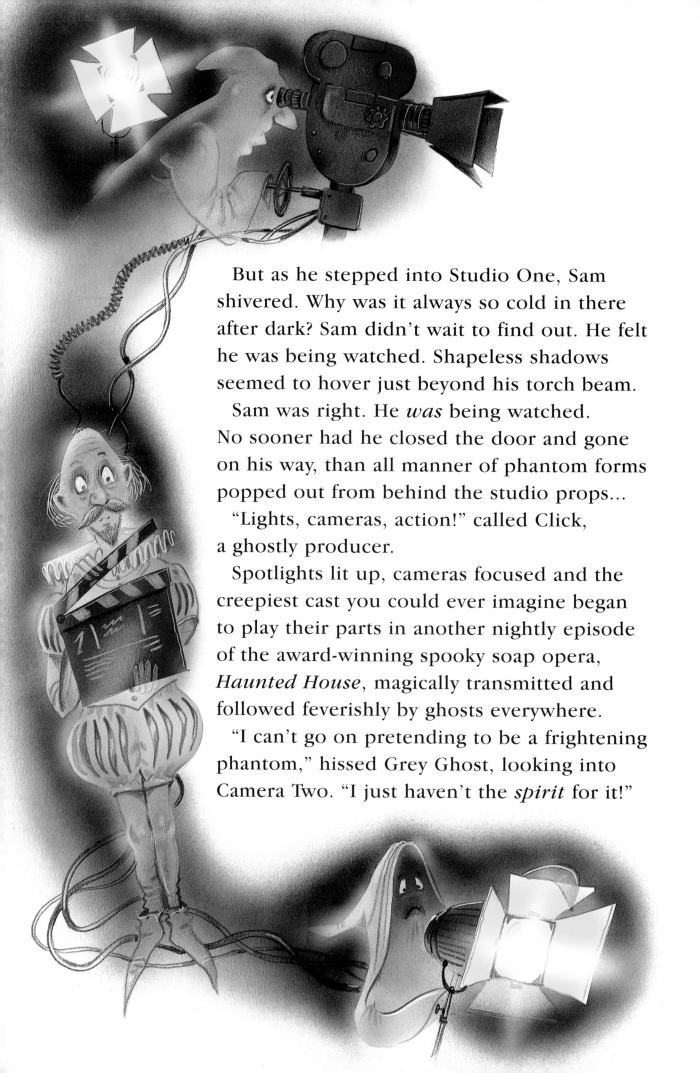

But as he stepped into Studio One, Sam shivered. Why was it always so cold in there after dark? Sam didn't wait to find out. He felt he was being watched. Shapeless shadows seemed to hover just beyond his torch beam.

Sam was right. He *was* being watched. No sooner had he closed the door and gone on his way, than all manner of phantom forms popped out from behind the studio props...

"Lights, cameras, action!" called Click, a ghostly producer.

Spotlights lit up, cameras focused and the creepiest cast you could ever imagine began to play their parts in another nightly episode of the award-winning spooky soap opera, *Haunted House*, magically transmitted and followed feverishly by ghosts everywhere.

"I can't go on pretending to be a frightening phantom," hissed Grey Ghost, looking into Camera Two. "I just haven't the *spirit* for it!"

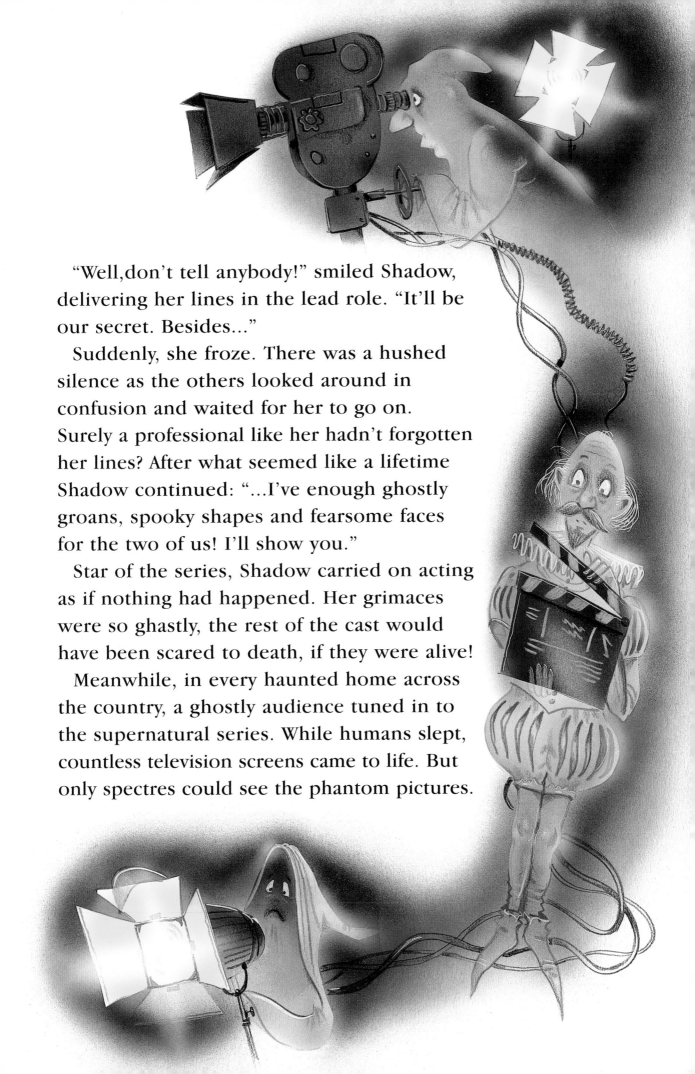

"Well, don't tell anybody!" smiled Shadow, delivering her lines in the lead role. "It'll be our secret. Besides..."

Suddenly, she froze. There was a hushed silence as the others looked around in confusion and waited for her to go on. Surely a professional like her hadn't forgotten her lines? After what seemed like a lifetime Shadow continued: "...I've enough ghostly groans, spooky shapes and fearsome faces for the two of us! I'll show you."

Star of the series, Shadow carried on acting as if nothing had happened. Her grimaces were so ghastly, the rest of the cast would have been scared to death, if they were alive!

Meanwhile, in every haunted home across the country, a ghostly audience tuned in to the supernatural series. While humans slept, countless television screens came to life. But only spectres could see the phantom pictures.

Back at the studios, another episode ended.

"Cut! Another out-of-this-world performance, Shadow!" said Click. "You're the star of the show! But you had us all worried there for a spell."

The other spooks gathered around. Shadow looked even more deathly white than usual.

"What's wrong?" asked Grey Ghost, gliding towards her like swirling smoke. "You froze — that's not like you!"

"I'm afraid I can't go on any more. I'm going to have to leave the show," said Shadow, unhappily.

The studio echoed eerily with shocked gasps.

"You, leave? Impossible!" cried Click. "Name whatever you want to stay and it's yours!"

"I'm sorry, but there's nothing you can give me," said Shadow. "I've lost my lucky wishbone. I've always kept it near me while I'm acting. The studio cleaners must have swept it up and thrown it away."

Shadow shook her head and floated wearily into a chair. The other ghosts hovered anxiously around.

"I can't go on without it," said Shadow. "If I were human, you'd say I'd lost my nerve. Why, I wobble like jelly as soon as I see a camera! Without my lucky wishbone, I always get stage fright!"

Click gently touched Shadow's frosty cheek with a crooked, bony finger.

"You've been working too hard," he smiled. "What you need is a party to cheer you up!"

So the next night as soon as the cameras stopped rolling they threw a huge party for Shadow. The creepy cast did all they could to make her feel better. Two ghosts slipped into a pantomime horse from the costume department and galloped through the air. Then a spectral blob called Slimy slithered about, changing shape. He dripped down the walls and spread like shiny, green goo across the floor. Knuckles, a skeleton, pretended to step on him and slip over.

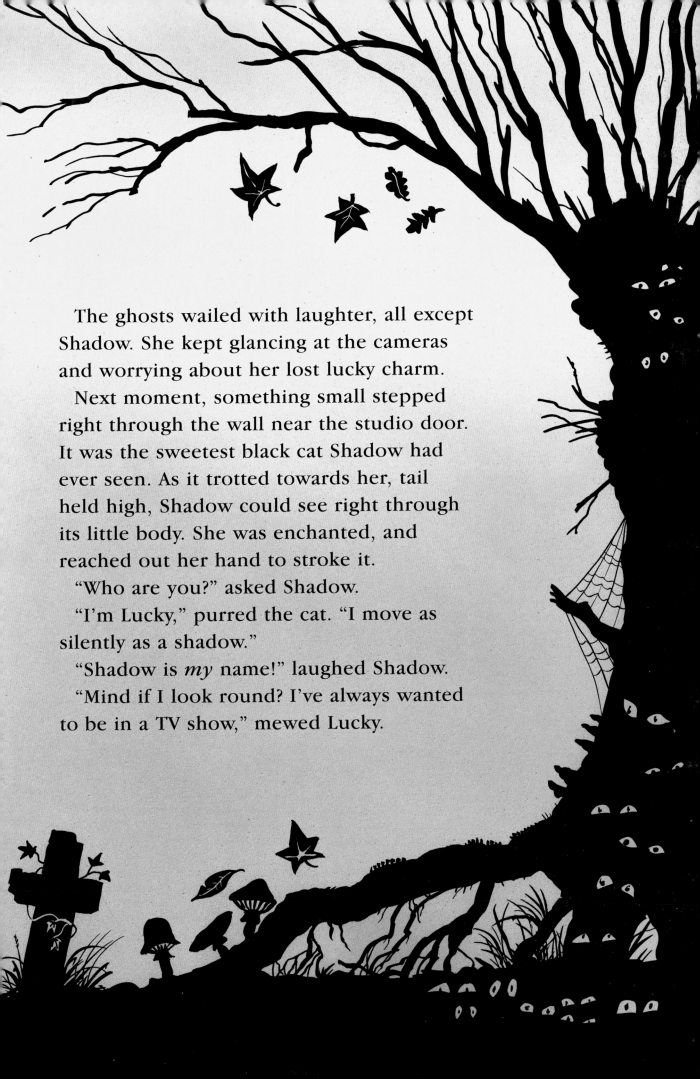

The ghosts wailed with laughter, all except Shadow. She kept glancing at the cameras and worrying about her lost lucky charm.

Next moment, something small stepped right through the wall near the studio door. It was the sweetest black cat Shadow had ever seen. As it trotted towards her, tail held high, Shadow could see right through its little body. She was enchanted, and reached out her hand to stroke it.

"Who are you?" asked Shadow.

"I'm Lucky," purred the cat. "I move as silently as a shadow."

"Shadow is *my* name!" laughed Shadow.

"Mind if I look round? I've always wanted to be in a TV show," mewed Lucky.

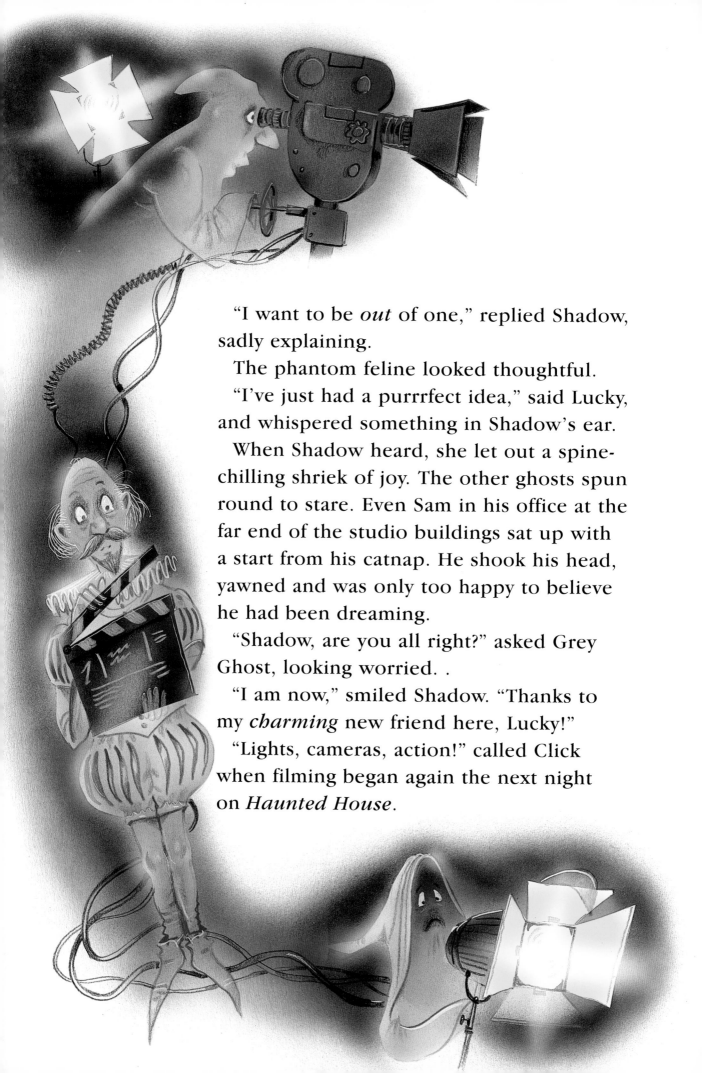

"I want to be *out* of one," replied Shadow, sadly explaining.

The phantom feline looked thoughtful.

"I've just had a purrrfect idea," said Lucky, and whispered something in Shadow's ear.

When Shadow heard, she let out a spine-chilling shriek of joy. The other ghosts spun round to stare. Even Sam in his office at the far end of the studio buildings sat up with a start from his catnap. He shook his head, yawned and was only too happy to believe he had been dreaming.

"Shadow, are you all right?" asked Grey Ghost, looking worried. .

"I am now," smiled Shadow. "Thanks to my *charming* new friend here, Lucky!"

"Lights, cameras, action!" called Click when filming began again the next night on *Haunted House*.

This time, joining the high-spirited
cast of regular spectres, there was an
extra ghost. Lucky was delighted to have
been given a glide-on part. Shadow was
even happier about it. Her faultless
performance proved it. After all, Shadow
had a new lucky charm. And as for any
stage fright, there simply wasn't a *ghost*
of a chance it would return now!

Spooky Spells

"It's almost Halloween again," said Snitchy Witch to her black cat Treacle. "How the time has flown! And I still haven't quite finished making the food for the Witches Convention. I must do it today."

So she sat down at the table and started to write her shopping list which went something like this: *2 newts; 3 frogs; bag of snails; tin of slug juice; 1 rat's tail; packet of mixed spiders…* She was so busy writing that she didn't notice the little ghost watching her carefully from behind the cauldron…

Now, Halloween, as you all know, is a very special time for witches, and this witch was no exception. In fact, this Halloween was *extra* special for Snitchy Witch as she was hosting the WESTERN WITCHES ANNUAL HALLOWEEN CONVENTION. She was holding it in the ballroom of the Haunted House, hired specially for the occasion. Witches were coming from far and wide to attend lectures on important topics, such as *Magic Brooms and How to Handle Them*; *Growing Warts in a Week* and *If you Want to Get Ahead, Get a Cat!*

The highlight of the event would be a *Spelling Contest*, where the witches would compete for the coveted title of WITCH OF THE YEAR.

"Just wait until it's my turn," said Snitchy Witch as she finished her list. "I'll show 'em a thing or two!" and she hurried off on her broomstick to the shops.

As soon as he was sure she had gone, Spooky, the little ghost, came out from behind the cauldron. He didn't like stinky witches. Having just one in the Haunted House was bad enough — but a whole convention! It was no use trying to frighten them away — witches weren't afraid of a little ghost like him. But perhaps there was a way to make them scare themselves… Spooky smiled. He would certainly have some fun with those silly old witches…

Snitchy Witch returned from her shopping expedition and spent the rest of the day carefully cooking up the most disgusting food she could think of. Then she dusted off her spellbook and polished up her favourite magic wand. She could hardly wait to demonstrate her spectacular 'garden slug into gigantic gooey chocolate cake' spell! And all the time she was busy preparing, Spooky was busy watching her...

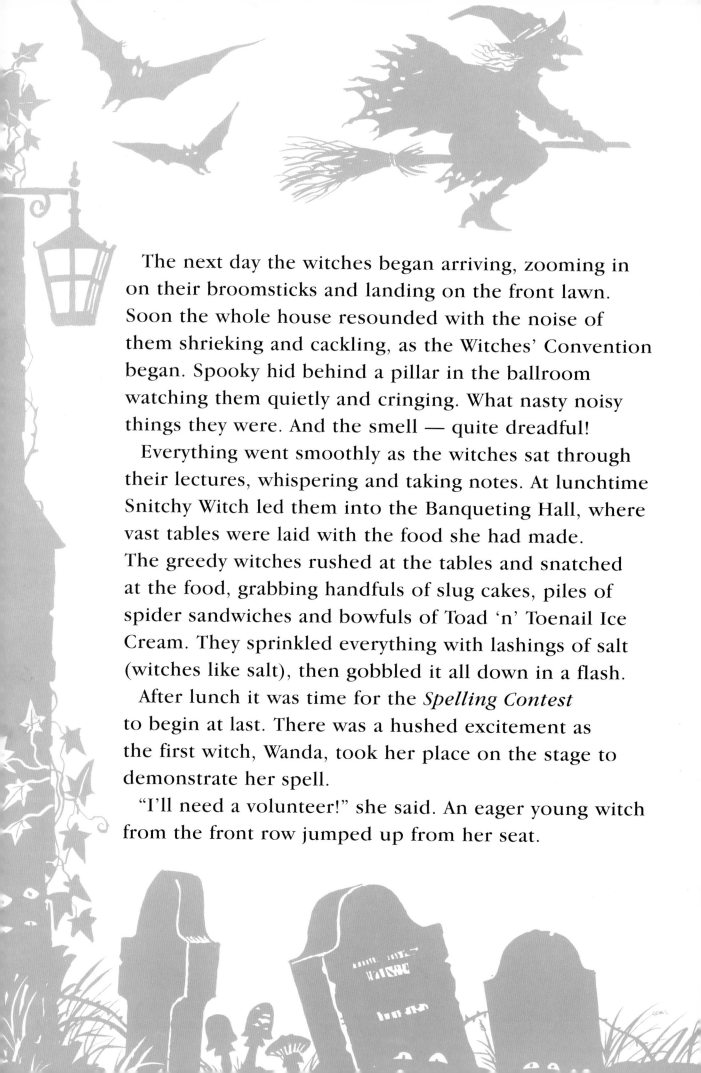

The next day the witches began arriving, zooming in on their broomsticks and landing on the front lawn. Soon the whole house resounded with the noise of them shrieking and cackling, as the Witches' Convention began. Spooky hid behind a pillar in the ballroom watching them quietly and cringing. What nasty noisy things they were. And the smell — quite dreadful!

Everything went smoothly as the witches sat through their lectures, whispering and taking notes. At lunchtime Snitchy Witch led them into the Banqueting Hall, where vast tables were laid with the food she had made. The greedy witches rushed at the tables and snatched at the food, grabbing handfuls of slug cakes, piles of spider sandwiches and bowfuls of Toad 'n' Toenail Ice Cream. They sprinkled everything with lashings of salt (witches like salt), then gobbled it all down in a flash.

After lunch it was time for the *Spelling Contest* to begin at last. There was a hushed excitement as the first witch, Wanda, took her place on the stage to demonstrate her spell.

"I'll need a volunteer!" she said. An eager young witch from the front row jumped up from her seat.

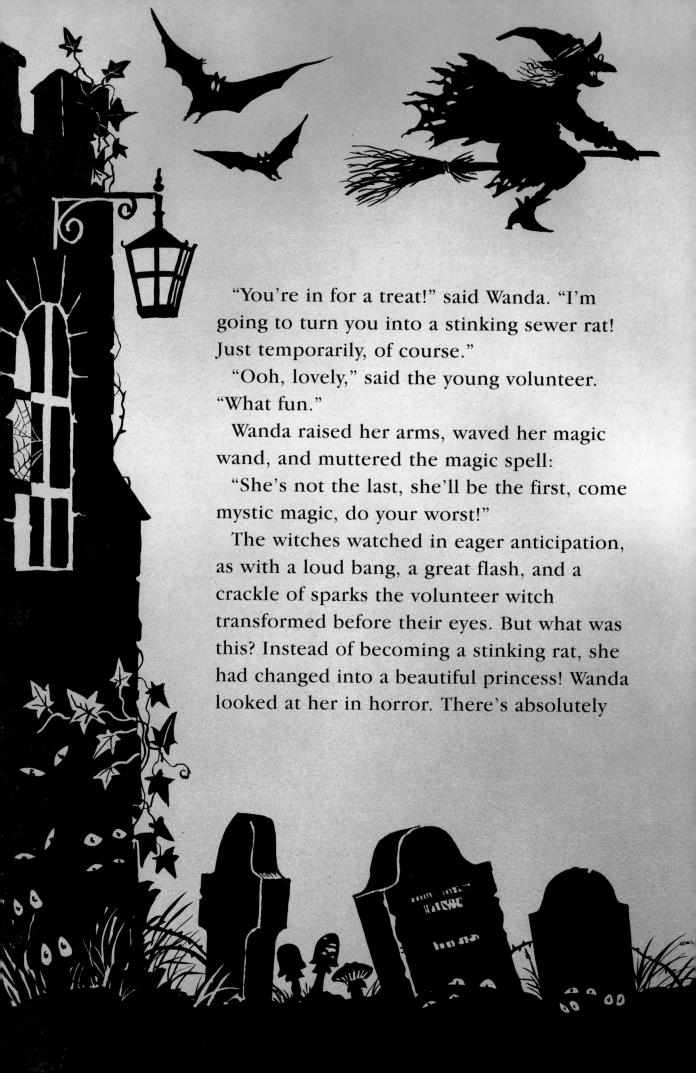

"You're in for a treat!" said Wanda. "I'm going to turn you into a stinking sewer rat! Just temporarily, of course."

"Ooh, lovely," said the young volunteer. "What fun."

Wanda raised her arms, waved her magic wand, and muttered the magic spell:

"She's not the last, she'll be the first, come mystic magic, do your worst!"

The witches watched in eager anticipation, as with a loud bang, a great flash, and a crackle of sparks the volunteer witch transformed before their eyes. But what was this? Instead of becoming a stinking rat, she had changed into a beautiful princess! Wanda looked at her in horror. There's absolutely

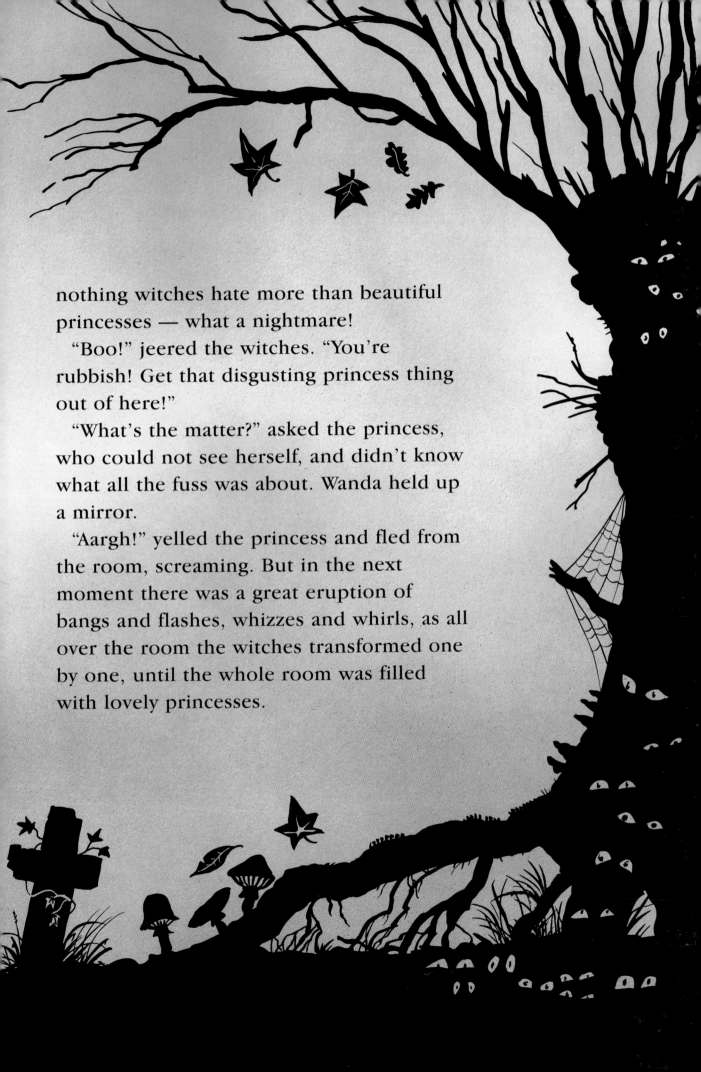

nothing witches hate more than beautiful princesses — what a nightmare!

"Boo!" jeered the witches. "You're rubbish! Get that disgusting princess thing out of here!"

"What's the matter?" asked the princess, who could not see herself, and didn't know what all the fuss was about. Wanda held up a mirror.

"Aargh!" yelled the princess and fled from the room, screaming. But in the next moment there was a great eruption of bangs and flashes, whizzes and whirls, as all over the room the witches transformed one by one, until the whole room was filled with lovely princesses.

Then, what a fuss and commotion! They hollered and screamed and jumped up and down, clutching at their shiny hair and beautiful gowns. Spooky laughed and laughed until he cried, for of course the commotion was all his fault. He had made a spell for beautiful princesses which he had found at the back of Snitchy Witch's spell book while she was out shopping. "Only to be used on your worst enemies, or in emergencies," it had said. Spooky decided this was definitely an emergency, and had added the spell to the salt (which, as you remember, the witches had used plenty of on their lunch!).

Still yelling and screaming (most unladylike!) the princesses leapt on their brooms and fled.

"Come back!" yelled Snitchy Witch (now transformed into a princess herself). "We haven't finished the contest!" But it was no use. The witches, or rather princesses, had gone. Spooky stretched out on an old sofa with a satisfied grin on his face. Peace and quiet once more. Only one stinky witch left in the Haunted House, and even she wasn't too bad now she was a princess!

Stand and Deliver

It was a dark and stormy night. Thunder crashed, rain lashed, lightning flashed and, jolting along inside the royal horse and carriage, poor King Penniless felt bruised and bashed!

He had been away on important business, trying unsuccessfully to raise funds to help save his crumbling castle from falling apart. For although he was a king, he was not a wealthy one, having lost all his money in a series of bad investments. He was a kind and gentle king, but he had no head for business. King Penniless leaned back inside his carriage and closed his eyes. What could he do to save himself from ruin?

The royal horse and carriage battled on along the bumpy road that crossed the wild and windy moor. The glass rattled in the carriage windows, and a steady stream of water poured in through a leak in the roof, and dripped onto the king's head.

"What a sorry state to be in," the king thought, miserably. Just then, with a loud whinny, the horses reared up in fright,

and the carriage came crashing to a halt.

"Stand and deliver!" boomed an eerie
voice outside. King Penniless nervously
lowered the window and peered out into
the stormy night, but it was so dark that he
couldn't see anything at all. "What's the
matter?" the king called to his coachman,
trying to sound braver than he felt.

"It.. it's the Gh-ghostly Highwayman!"
stuttered his terrified coachman in reply.

"Ghosts, bish-bosh!" called King Penniless,
crossly. "It's just the wind. Drive on!"

"I c-can't sir," replied the coachman.
"We've lost a wheel."

"Well, hurry up and replace it!" ordered
the king. This was all he needed! He was
tired and worn out with worry, and he just
wanted to get home, put his feet up and
have a nice hot cup of cocoa.

The king climbed down out of the carriage to go and see what all the fuss was about for himself. Just then a great flash of lightning lit up the sky, illuminating the moors. And there, right in front of the king, sat the Ghostly Highwayman, perched high upon a pure white horse.

"Stand and deliver — your money or your life!" he cried. His cape swirled around his ashen face, as he pointed an old-fashioned pistol at the king.

Well, the poor king trembled so hard that his teeth started to chatter.

"B..but I d..don't have any money!" he stuttered.

"Nonsense!" cried the Highwayman. "You're the king aren't you?"

"Y-yes — but I'm nearly bankrupt," said the king, and as it seemed there was nothing else for it, he went on to explain his position to his ghostly listener.

By the time the king had finished telling him the story of all his troubles, the Ghostly Highwayman was almost in tears. "How terrible for you," he said. "But there must be some way I can help. Let's think of a plan!"

"Help!" spluttered the king. "Why would you want to help? A moment ago you were threatening to shoot me!"

"I'm sorry. I didn't mean it," said the Ghostly Highwayman. "It's just part of the act. That's what highwaymen are supposed to say. I only stopped your carriage because it's lonely out here, and I wanted someone to talk to."

"Well there are better ways of making friends than waving pistols at people!" said the king, indignantly.

"You're right," said the ghost. "It's just that being a highwayman is all I know, although I was never very good at it — I suppose that's why I got caught. And it was thanks to your great-grandfather that I escaped the gallows, so really I owe you a favour."

He went on to explain how the king's great-grandfather had granted him a royal pardon, after his daughter, the young Princess Angelina,

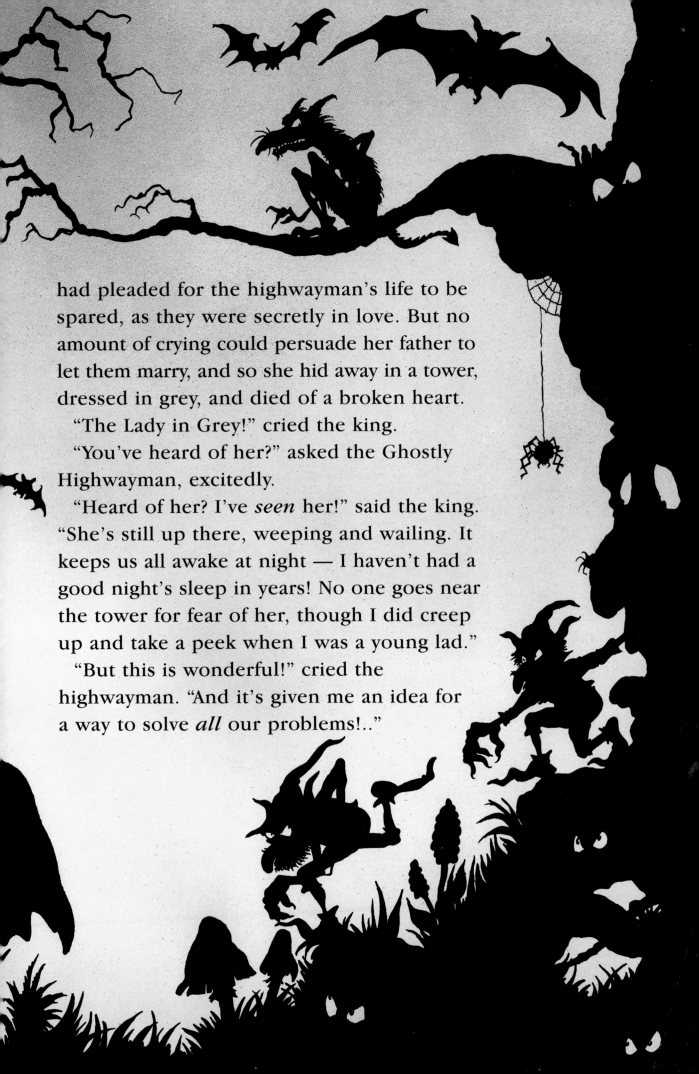

had pleaded for the highwayman's life to be spared, as they were secretly in love. But no amount of crying could persuade her father to let them marry, and so she hid away in a tower, dressed in grey, and died of a broken heart.

"The Lady in Grey!" cried the king.

"You've heard of her?" asked the Ghostly Highwayman, excitedly.

"Heard of her? I've *seen* her!" said the king. "She's still up there, weeping and wailing. It keeps us all awake at night — I haven't had a good night's sleep in years! No one goes near the tower for fear of her, though I did creep up and take a peek when I was a young lad."

"But this is wonderful!" cried the highwayman. "And it's given me an idea for a way to solve *all* our problems!.."

"Stand and deliver! Your money or your life!" boomed the Ghostly Highwayman. The two middle-aged ladies squealed with terror and delight, and quickly handed over their entrance fee for a place on the next tour of the haunted royal castle! The Lady in Grey smiled and winked at the highwayman as she stepped through the wall, let out a ghostly wail, and glided up the staircase. "Follow me!" she called. An eager bunch of tourists clambered up the stairs behind her, watched happily by the king, as he counted the day's takings.

"At this rate, the castle will be restored in no time!" said the king to the Ghostly Highwayman, rubbing his hands together in delight. "How can I ever thank you?"

"Being reunited with the Princess is reward enough," said the Ghostly Highwayman.

"Plus I don't have to live out on that windy moor any longer, holding people up just to have someone to talk to. There's only one thing more I could wish for — Princess Angelina's hand in marriage."

"Brilliant!" said the king. "A ghostly royal wedding. Now that should really bring in the crowds!.."

And as the king settled down to sleep that night, he gave a contented sigh. At last he could sleep in peace!

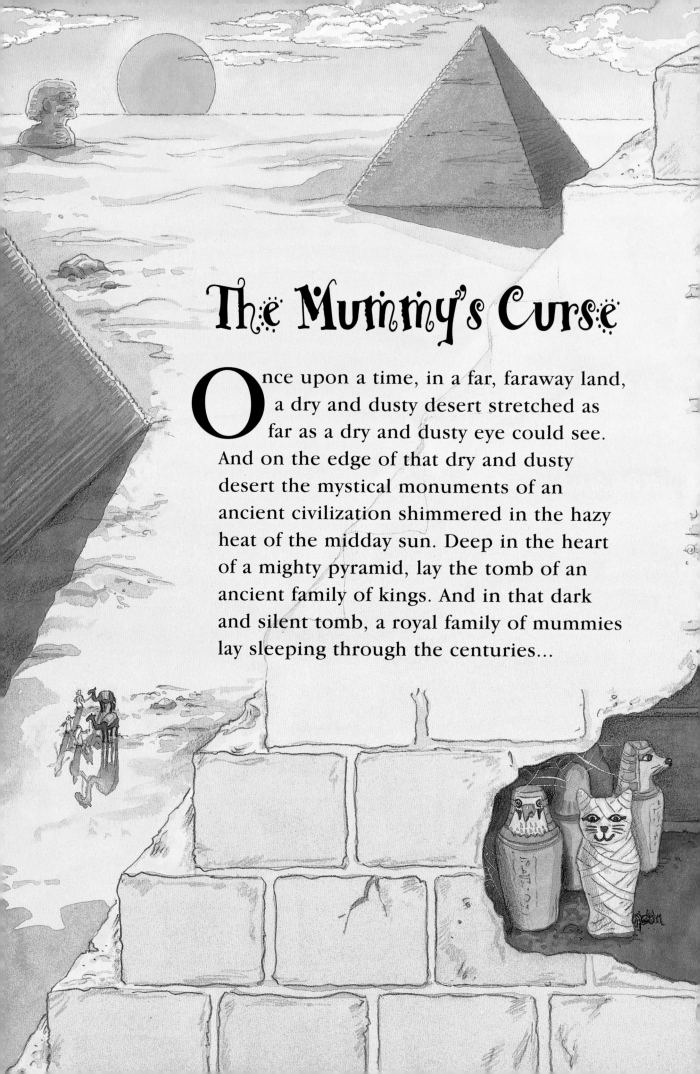

The Mummy's Curse

Once upon a time, in a far, faraway land, a dry and dusty desert stretched as far as a dry and dusty eye could see. And on the edge of that dry and dusty desert the mystical monuments of an ancient civilization shimmered in the hazy heat of the midday sun. Deep in the heart of a mighty pyramid, lay the tomb of an ancient family of kings. And in that dark and silent tomb, a royal family of mummies lay sleeping through the centuries...

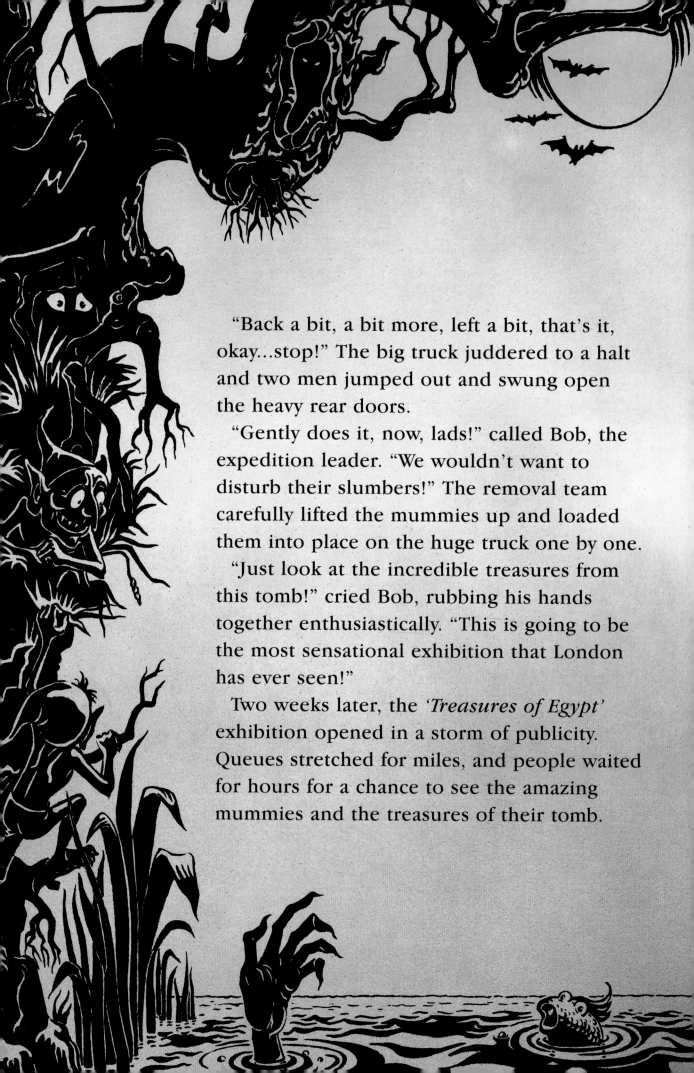

"Back a bit, a bit more, left a bit, that's it, okay...stop!" The big truck juddered to a halt and two men jumped out and swung open the heavy rear doors.

"Gently does it, now, lads!" called Bob, the expedition leader. "We wouldn't want to disturb their slumbers!" The removal team carefully lifted the mummies up and loaded them into place on the huge truck one by one.

"Just look at the incredible treasures from this tomb!" cried Bob, rubbing his hands together enthusiastically. "This is going to be the most sensational exhibition that London has ever seen!"

Two weeks later, the *'Treasures of Egypt'* exhibition opened in a storm of publicity. Queues stretched for miles, and people waited for hours for a chance to see the amazing mummies and the treasures of their tomb.

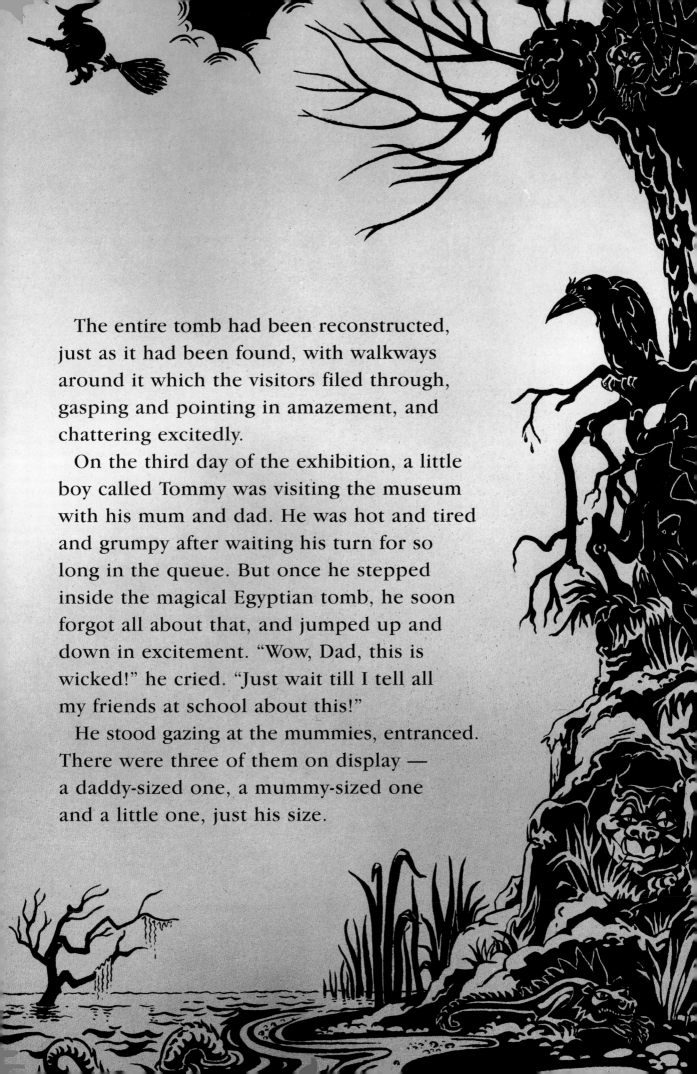

The entire tomb had been reconstructed, just as it had been found, with walkways around it which the visitors filed through, gasping and pointing in amazement, and chattering excitedly.

On the third day of the exhibition, a little boy called Tommy was visiting the museum with his mum and dad. He was hot and tired and grumpy after waiting his turn for so long in the queue. But once he stepped inside the magical Egyptian tomb, he soon forgot all about that, and jumped up and down in excitement. "Wow, Dad, this is wicked!" he cried. "Just wait till I tell all my friends at school about this!"

He stood gazing at the mummies, entranced. There were three of them on display — a daddy-sized one, a mummy-sized one and a little one, just his size.

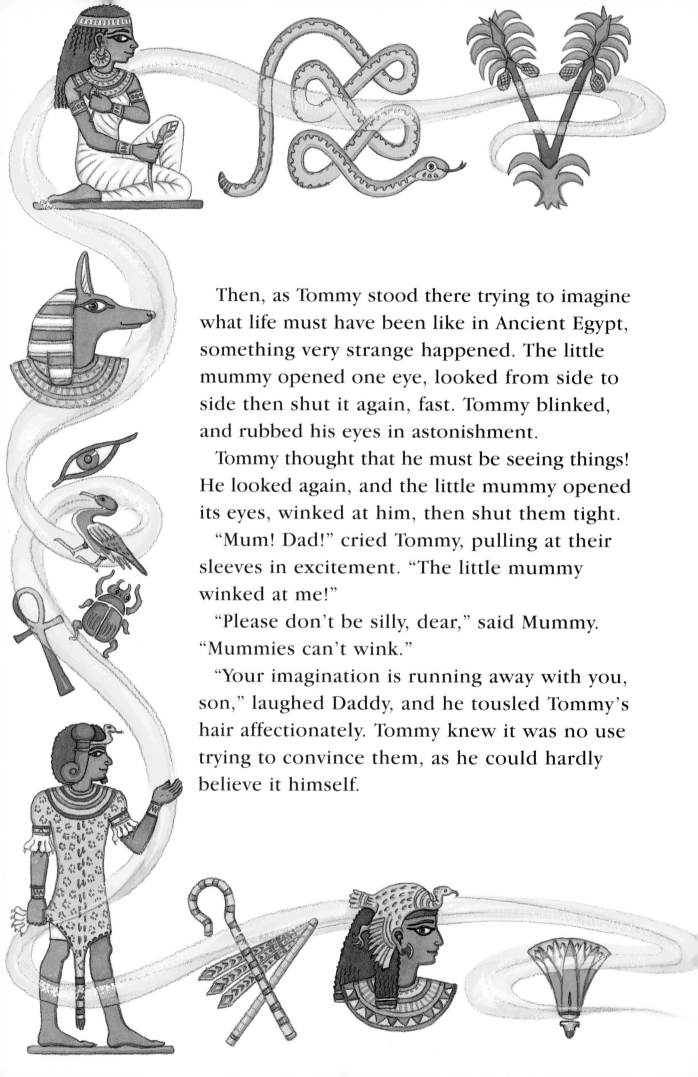

Then, as Tommy stood there trying to imagine what life must have been like in Ancient Egypt, something very strange happened. The little mummy opened one eye, looked from side to side then shut it again, fast. Tommy blinked, and rubbed his eyes in astonishment.

Tommy thought that he must be seeing things! He looked again, and the little mummy opened its eyes, winked at him, then shut them tight.

"Mum! Dad!" cried Tommy, pulling at their sleeves in excitement. "The little mummy winked at me!"

"Please don't be silly, dear," said Mummy. "Mummies can't wink."

"Your imagination is running away with you, son," laughed Daddy, and he tousled Tommy's hair affectionately. Tommy knew it was no use trying to convince them, as he could hardly believe it himself.

He wanted to stay and see if the little mummy would open his eyes again, but there was a big crowd behind him and he had to move along.

Meanwhile, the little mummy was feeling hot and tired and very confused himself. He had woken up in the night and looked around inside the tomb. It seemed as though he had been asleep forever. He yawned and stretched. He could see his mummy and daddy lying alongside him. Better wait for them to wake up too, so he laid back down and went to sleep.

Next morning the little mummy had been woken by a lot of noise. He opened one eye — who were all these odd-looking people, with strange bright-coloured garments, all staring at him and pointing? He shut his eye again fast. But just to make sure he wasn't seeing things he opened both his eyes again.

A little boy was standing right in front of him, looking at him in amazement. He looked friendly, so the mummy winked at him, then shut his eyes again tight. Perhaps if he stayed very still they would all go away.

But they didn't go away. The noise got louder and louder, and the little mummy got hotter and hotter. He felt stiff and uncomfortable and he was dying to stretch his legs. He took one more peek and decided the strange people looked friendly enough, so he plucked up his courage and with a great creak he climbed out of his case.

Well, there was pandemonium! People screamed and ran, some fainted, others stood frozen to the spot. Someone pulled the fire alarm and guards came running from every corner. The little mummy was terrified — whatever was going on? He ran from the room and out into the museum, his bandages trailing behind him. People screeched and fled, scattering in all directions as he came running towards them.

Sitting in the coffee shop with his mum and dad, Tommy watched as the little mummy ran past heading for the section on Ancient China.

"I told you he winked!" said Tommy to his astonished parents, leaping up from the table. Nearby, the museum guards were all arguing about who should try to catch the little mummy. No one wanted to volunteer.

"I'll go," said Tommy and, before anyone could stop him, he raced off in the direction the little mummy had taken. He had to search through Ancient China, South America, India and Greece before he found him hiding inside a Roman temple.

"Where am I? I want my mummy!" said the mummy, starting to cry.

"Don't worry," said Tommy. "I'll take you to her!" Tommy led the little mummy back, trying to explain where they were. The poor mummy was very confused, as everything looked so odd. Crowds cowered behind statues and pillars as they passed, marvelling at Tommy's bravery.

Before long the little mummy was back in his tomb. "I want to go home!" he said to Tommy.

"Just climb in your case and go back to sleep, and I'm sure you'll soon be there," said Tommy.

And that is just what happened. Scientists came from all over the world, but though they poked and prodded, and did all kinds of tests, nothing would make the little mummy wake up again. The exhibition was closed, and soon the mummies were back in Egypt, restored to their tomb. Tommy became a national hero and had his picture in all the newspapers.

And as for Bob, the expedition leader? "That exhibition certainly was sensational!" he said.

Peg's Pepper

Think of a witch and the chances are you'll imagine one with a big, black cat, just like Peg and her cat, Pepper. Peg lived in a crooked cottage, deep in a wood. She spent her time making bubbling brews and spectacular spells, which didn't always work. Elves and fairies would ask her to cure anything from a sore tooth to a broken wing. So Peg's time passed busily enough.

She was never lonely either, not with Pepper purring about the place. He followed Peg everywhere. If the witch was in her garden, gathering herbs or other more unpleasant ingredients for the cauldron, Pepper would stalk her through the long grass then pop out playfully. If Peg was sitting by the fire, studying her spell book, then Pepper would curl up contentedly on the witch's lap.

Even when Peg took night flights on her broomstick, Pepper tagged along. He would sink his sharp claws into the handle to get a good grip. Then Peg and Pepper would whizz away up past the moon.

The truth was, Peg and Pepper were perfect company for each other. That is, until something rather strange happened.

"A...atchooo!" Peg suddenly sneezed as she sat gently brushing Pepper's dark fur which shone like polished coal. The witch's long nose began to itch and twitch and her eyes started to water.

"Tsk! Don't tell me I've caught a cold," she said. "I shouldn't have stayed out late last night, chasing shooting stars on my broomstick. It was much too chilly. A...ATCHOOOO!"

This time, Peg sneezed so hard her pointed hat slipped over her eyes. Pepper miaowed sympathetically while the witch went to get a handkerchief from the washing line.

Outside in the fresh air, she stopped sneezing straight away. But Pepper followed Peg outside. He brushed against her, hoping to be stroked. No sooner had Peg obliged when she sneezed again; not once, not twice, but three times. Back indoors, it was even worse. Whenever Pepper came too close, Peg started sneezing.

"It's you, Pepper! You're making me sneeze!" wailed the witch. "I've become allergic to you!"

What a *cat*astrophe! Something had to be done and quick-thinking Peg knew just what.

Peg fetched her wand as Pepper looked at her, puzzled.

"Don't worry," said Peg. "You'll still be my constant companion. It's just that, to stop me sneezing, you must swap your fur for feathers!"

The witch waved her wand and uttered something about: "...the strangest cat you've ever heard, now, let Pepper become a bird!"

He did, too. Gone were Pepper's whiskers, purrs and paws. In their place were bill, claws and 'caws' as Pepper turned into a bright-eyed crow. Flapping new-found wings, he clumsily took off across the room. But flying takes practise. Pepper sent some herbs, hung up to dry, dropping down on Peg's head. More fell into the cauldron. They made Peg's latest concoction spill over the brim in a gooey, spreading puddle of sticky slime.

All the time Pepper continued his noisy, non-stop 'cawing'. The ear-splitting racket made the poor exasperated witch wince.

"Stop, stop!" she cried.

But Pepper couldn't stop himself – it was part of being a crow, after all. So Peg was in a fine flap, too. She rushed to her faithful spell book and quickly hunted for another spell.

With a 'POP!', Peg turned Pepper into a toad. He sat, somewhat confused, with big, bulging eyes, on the tabletop. Peg stroked him gently.

"There, there!" she soothed. "I know warty skin isn't a patch on soft, silky fur, Pepper. But at least I've stopped sneezing and you're so much quieter now!"

Pepper hopped unhappily across the flagstone floor then disappeared behind some boxes and bottles. Peg searched everywhere, but Pepper was nowhere to be found.

"He's sulking," thought Peg. "But what else could I do?"

Probably the only place Peg didn't look for Pepper was in her pointed hat, resting on its

side by her broomstick. Later, when the witch put it on, Pepper landed on her head with a squelch. He gave Peg such a shock that she dropped her wand and spent the next half-hour hunting for that instead.

That evening, Pepper squatted silently on Peg's lap. If he felt miserable, so did she. After all, a toad just wasn't the same as a cuddly cat. Peg was just beginning to think that she might be better off trying to live with the sneezing, when another idea came to her in a flash. Instead of changing Pepper, she would try changing her nose! She whisked up a magic spell in no time and with a WHIZZ! BANG! her large pointed nose changed into a small dainty one.

A further flash from her crooked fingertip spelled goodbye toad and hello cat again. The witch waited eagerly to see if her new nose would solve the problem. Success! Peg didn't sneeze once.

"Magic!" she grinned.

Pepper was delighted to be back to his usual, furry self.

"Not even a tickle from my new, little nose!" cackled Peg, picking up Pepper and stroking him. "I'm cured!"

Pepper purred loudly. But Peg suddenly stopped laughing and uttered a faint sound.

"Hic!"

At the same time, Pepper felt Peg's shoulders shake. It only lasted a moment. But then it happened again, and again.

"Hic! Hic!" The sound only stopped when Peg put Pepper down.

"Great slithering slugs!" shrieked the witch. "My spell's misfired! Now see what you make me do, Pepper!"

But Pepper didn't wait to see anything!
He'd had more than his share of changing
shape for one day. The last thing he
wanted was to be turned into a rat,
hedgehog, or anything else Peg may care
to think of. Pepper hurtled outside while
Peg rushed for her spell book. Thumbing
through Magic Cures, she looked up the
letter 'H'.

"'Hairy hands, horrible howls'," she read,
urgently. "I know it's here somewhere.
How *do* you spell hiccups?!"

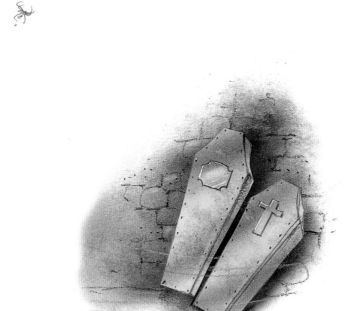